dear Unc,

Enjoy!

—manda
xmas '01

LENIN LIVES!

LENIN LIVES!

a novel by
Gregory O'Brien

STEIN AND DAY / *Publishers* / New York

This story is fiction.
With the exception of public
figures, all other names
are purely coincidental.

First published in 1984
Copyright © 1984 by Gregory C. O'Brien, Jr.
All rights reserved, Stein and Day, Incorporated
Designed by Louis A. Ditizio
Printed in the United States of America
STEIN AND DAY/*Publishers*
Scarborough House
Briarcliff Manor, N.Y. 10510

Library of Congress Cataloging in Publication Data

O'Brien, Gregory.
   Lenin lives!

   1. Lenin, Vladimir Il'ich, 1870–1924—Fiction.
I. Title.
PS 3565.B669L4   1984   813′.54   83-40369
ISBN 0-8128-2949-2

To Mom and Dad, who encouraged
me to give words to the idea, and for
Carolyn, Kelly, Jeffrey, and Tricia

LENIN LIVES!

FIRST DAY

A.M.

MOSCOW (AP)—Taking what may be the greatest political gamble of the twentieth century, Soviet officials here today claimed they have performed a medical feat of sensational proportions: the resurrection of Russian revolutionary leader V. I. Lenin, who died exactly sixty years ago.

Straight-faced Kremlin leaders, including General Secretary Chernenko, appeared before a capacity crowd of foreign correspondents and diplomats, who sat in collective stunned silence while Russian physician Oleg Borchezk delivered a prepared announcement containing little detail.

Few questions were permitted once the announcement was completed. However, officials did promise to produce the Soviet hero, known as the father of Russian communism, "when it becomes appropriate." No indication was given as to when this might be.

Soon after the press briefing, a similar announcement was carried by the Soviet news agency Tass. For the most part, visible reaction among Russians going about their everyday activities has been subdued. Several hundred puzzled Muscovites did gather briefly near the famed leader's tomb in Red Square, which has been closed for the past six weeks, allegedly for repairs.

Reaction among foreigners here has been universally skeptical, prompting a rash of black humor in the hours immediately following the announcement. . . .

P.M.

WASHINGTON (AP)—Asked today for a reaction to the Soviet claim that medical scientists there have resurrected former Premier V. I. Lenin, dead sixty years, President Reagan quipped, "And you folks used to kid me about 'Bedtime for Bonzo.' This has got to be the worst script of all time." Reagan's remark was indicative of official Washington, which has greeted the news with unrestrained mirth.

Other officials reached for comment included Senator John Tower (R-Texas), who called the announcement "absurd," and House Speaker Thomas P. O'Neill (D-Mass.), who said it "takes the cake." Meanwhile, religious leaders seemed to take some offense at the claim, the Rev. Billy Graham calling it "blasphemous. . . ."

PRAGUE (AP)—Eastern European leaders, perhaps caught off-guard by the Russian announcement concerning V. I. Lenin, have maintained tight-lipped silence, apparently hoping to get more facts before making a comment.

Popular reaction, though mixed, has been mainly doubtful. Nevertheless, official communist newspapers carrying a brief mention of the story were sold out only hours after appearing on newsstands here. Everywhere, the story has captivated public

13

interest seldom paralleled by any political event since the end of World War II.

Though officially an atheist country, several people greeted the news, not as the scientific event portrayed by official Moscow, but as a miracle of divine origin. One shopkeeper, on hearing the news, said quietly, "Christ is coming. . . ."

SECOND
DAY

LENIN: WORLD'S GREATEST
MODERN REVOLUTIONARY
By United Press International

In the wake of yesterday's stunning announcement in Moscow, many Americans today are asking, "Who was—or is—V. I. Lenin?"

To the disappointment of several celebrating New York teenagers arrested last night for disturbing the peace, Manhattan police have established that he is not related to the late Beatle singing star, John Lennon.

In the Soviet Union, however, Lenin is a combination of Abraham Lincoln, Muhammad Ali and Robert Redford. His face, bust and statue are ubiquitous, appearing in virtually every public building, park, square and railroad station. Since before his death in 1924, he has been that country's foremost hero.

Lenin was actually born Vladimir Ilyich Ulyanov in the Volga River town of Simbirsk a few months after the outbreak of the Franco-Prussian War in 1870. The third of six children, he was the son of an able and respected school instructor, who was promoted to the upper ranks of service nobility—the military equivalent of major general.

The mastermind of the Russian revolution probably saw little in his early youth of the social upheaval that would later turn him into a communist zealot. Reared to be a modest gentleman farmer, his life took a dramatic turn in 1881 when his older brother Aleksandr was hanged with five co-conspirators following an amateurish attempt on the life of Czar Nicholas II.

A brilliant student, the younger Ulyanov was bitter toward authority and at the same time captivated by communist rhetoric.

At Kazan University, he soon found himself embroiled in a student demonstration. When angry school officials expelled him, the enraged youth began to read the writings of Marx.

By 1893 Ulyanov had changed his name to Lenin. As an extern student, he had managed to win a law degree from the University of St. Petersburg; and now as a fledgling lawyer, Lenin joined a Marxist discussion group. Within two years, Lenin's revolutionary activities again got him into hot water with the czarist establishment, but this time his punishment was three years of exile in Siberia.

By 1905, Lenin was the self-proclaimed leader-in-exile of the Bolsheviks, urging "expropriations" or bank robberies to build up the revolutionaries' funds. Later he moved to Zurich, Switzerland, where during World War I he tried vainly to fan the flames of revolution in that neutral nation.

Following an often stormy relationship with his comrades, in 1917 he at last reentered Russia via Germany in a sealed railroad car to lead the assault on the czar's winter palace. Shortly after that historic victory, Lenin became "Chief of the People's Commissars," or premier of the Soviet government.

His views of government were harsh, perhaps ruthless, by today's Soviet standards, as were his opinions of religion. He once called "the notion of a lord God . . . an unspeakable abomination . . . and loathsome pestilence."

Lenin ruled Russia as the first among equals with Leon Trotsky and Joseph Stalin until the aftereffects of a stroke killed him in 1924.

Given the most elaborate funeral in the history of the world, for nearly six decades the Russian figure has lain in state in Moscow's Red Square. In the intervening years, it is estimated that up to eighty-five million Russians and foreign tourists have silently marched by his casket, many moved by his lifelike presence.

Almost eerily prophetic, banners and billboards everywhere for three-score years have proclaimed the epitaph, "Lenin Lived, Lenin Lives, Lenin Will Live!"

U.S. SCIENTISTS DOUBT
SOVIET MIRACLE CLAIM
By Times Bureaus

BOSTON—Four leading American physicians contacted here are highly skeptical of the claim made yesterday by Soviet officials concerning the resurrection of their country's former leader, V. I. Lenin.

Speaking on behalf of the American Board of Pathology, Dr. Abraham Greenberg of the Johns Hopkins School of Medicine put the matter succinctly: "From what we know of Soviet science, such a feat is not possible." Lenin died in 1924, Greenberg pointed out, compounding "by several orders of magnitude" the chances of rehabilitating his corpse.

"Regardless of the exterior preservation of the body, his cells, organs, tissues—everything, really—would have deteriorated far beyond the ability of the most modern technology to regenerate it."

An even blunter appraisal was offered by Dr. C. Dixon Hawley of the Stanford Medical School. "This story is pure hokum; a hoax for some obscure political purpose. I am astounded that they assume it would have any credibility whatsoever."

Agreeing with that view was Dr. Marcia Van Atter of the University of Chicago School of Medicine. "I personally think the story is pure fiction. It would be funny if it weren't so sick."

Also contacted was Dr. Randolph Miceli of the University of North Carolina at Chapel Hill. "I would welcome the chance to examine Mr. Lenin, but somehow I suspect Western scientists will not be given that opportunity," Miceli said.

THIRD
DAY

A.M.

SOVIETS SILENT; WORLD ASKS: "WHERE'S LENIN?"

MOSCOW (UPI)—More than forty-eight hours have elapsed since Kremlin leaders startled the world with the news of Lenin's alleged resurrection.

Despite the open incredulity expressed here by virtually the entire international diplomatic community, no further announcement has been made regarding the long-deceased Soviet hero, giving rise to the speculation that the Russians are hesitant to produce the centerpiece of this dramatic story.

"Before the week is out, I expect you may see some red faces around here," said French chargé Louis du Toit. The diplomat, however, would not elaborate.

Meanwhile, life in this capital, always dreary at this time of year, continues as though the events of the past two days had not occurred. Beyond the initial news item contained in Pravda, there has been no mention of the story in the Soviet press. Strangely, too, Soviet television has not carried a single word regarding the sensational news briefing by officials here Tuesday. . . .

NEW YORK

THIS IS AN ABC NEWS BRIEF. I'M PETER JENNINGS. Extraordinary security precautions are being taken in the Kremlin at this hour, some believe, involving the dramatic story of V. I. Lenin. By audio, we now switch to ABC correspondent Pierre Salinger in Moscow.

THIS IS PIERRE SALINGER, PETER, CAN YOU HEAR me?

YES, PIERRE, YOU'RE . . .

PETER, AN INCREDIBLE SIGHT IS UNFOLDING BEfore us. I am with approximately two dozen correspondents representing various news agencies, gathered on the roof of the Rossiya Hotel near Red Square. For the past hour, tanks and armored vehicles have been pouring into this area, along with hundreds of infantry units in winter dress. I cannot tell you why, because frankly we aren't sure. But . . .

PIERRE, CAN YOU HEAR ME?

YES, PETER.

PIERRE, SPECULATION HERE IN NEW YORK IS that this has something to do with the Lenin story. What about it?

ABSOLUTELY IMPOSSIBLE TO SAY, BUT YES, SOME people here think so, too. Just a guess, really. We'll keep you posted.

THANK YOU, PIERRE. EVENTS ARE OBVIOUSLY A bit mysterious at this point, but ABC will continue to carry this story as long as there is something new to report. This is Peter Jennings in New York.

WASHINGTON

THE CHAIR RECOGNIZES THE GENTLEMAN FROM New York.

MR. SPEAKER, FOR THE PAST TWO DAYS THE RUS-sians have been silent about the reincarnation of V. I. Lenin. When we know the whole story, my guess is that it will be exposed as the most tasteless prank of all time. The point is though, Mr. Speaker, we should not let them get away with it. Frankly, I am disturbed that the administration has not handled this opportunity more deftly. The president's quip was amusing, perhaps, but hardly the kind of serious leadership that would capitalize on the story for all it's worth. . . .

WOULD THE GENTLEMAN YIELD?

I WILL YIELD ONE MINUTE TO MY DISTINGUISHED colleague from Tennessee. . . .

I WOULD LIKE TO KNOW WHAT IN THUNDER THE president is supposed to do with this, beyond keeping his trap shut and letting them dig themselves a deeper hole. Is everything so partisan in this city that we have to blame the president when the Russians want to make damn fools of themselves? . . ."

ATTENTION, EDITORS. KREMLIN LEADERS HAVE CALLED A PRESS BRIEFING AT THE MINISTRY OF INFORMATION, TOMORROW (FRIDAY), 0800 HOURS MOSCOW TIME. ACCREDITED CORRESPONDENTS ONLY. MORE LENIN STORY POSSIBLE.

FOURTH DAY

NEW YORK

I'M PETER JENNINGS. "GOOD MORNING AMERICA" will not be seen this morning in order to bring you this special news program. We switch you live to ABC Moscow correspondent Bob Zelnick.

THANK YOU, PETER. THE SCENE ON YOUR TELEVIsion screen was filmed just a few hours ago in Red Square. As you can see, hundreds of thousands of flag-waving Russians, many of them carrying flowers as well, were gathered for a spectacle of historic dimensions. As much as anything ever is in this tightly controlled capital, I must say this was a spontaneous event. Only this morning, Soviet television announced that Russian revolutionary leader V. I. Lenin would make a dramatic appearance before the world, in Red Square. Good to that word, at least, the Russians have produced someone who looks remarkably like the former premier, at least in old photographs. We have been collecting photographs of Lenin, I might add, since Tuesday's announcement. With audio, now, we listen to my colleague ABC foreign correspondent Pierre Salinger as he earlier described today's event.

THIS IS PIERRE SALINGER. THE CROWD BELOW

our scaffolding, erected for ABC, has been gathering for several hours. Although many are carrying flags and photographs of Lenin, it is not a noisy crowd. Perhaps this is because of the extraordinary security all around us. I believe our cameras can pan the square . . . yes . . . and now you see tanks, dozens perhaps, as well as militia. The soldiers here, however, have been in a festive mood . . . many smiles. . . .

Although it is only 25 degrees, Russians are used to cold weather and really do not seem to mind the chill. Our ABC camera crew is a little numb up here, however, and frankly, we'd just as soon something would happen to get the blood pumping. . . . Beach weather? Jack Warren, our technical director, says in Minnesota this is beach weather. Perhaps so, Jack. . . .

There you see several girls with flowers. Very pretty, some of these Russian girls—not at all the hefty stereotype of much Western humor. The noise level is rising. I detect . . . Peter, I believe we can see some movement on the outer edge of the square. A line of black limousines is moving into the square toward a reviewing stand erected here yesterday. Listen now and you can hear the strains of Russian music. Several military bands are in the area immediately to your left of the stand—yes, you can see them close up now, on your screen.

On our monitor we now see officials getting out of their cars. There is Marshal Nicolai Ogarkov, head of the Soviet high command. Now Foreign Minister Andrei Gromyko. As he approaches the stairs, we can see Party Secretary Konstantin U. Chernenko now beginning to ascend the staircase. Over the stand we see the banner so familiar here in the Soviet Union. Translated, it says, "Lenin Lived, Lenin Lives, Lenin Will Live."

The noise of the crowd is rising now. If you can still hear me, we see much of Soviet officialdom mounting the stand, Soviet generals and admirals. . . .

32

Now a cheer . . . more a roar, really. The noise here is quite deafening. Coming up the stairs is someone. . . . I still do not believe this is happening . . . an actor, I must say he is an actor, what else can one say at a time like this? . . . Who . . . who . . . well, I suppose he does look a bit like (cough) Lenin . . . more than a bit, really . . . this is incredible . . . calm, I should say confident-looking, really. . . .

Secretary Chernenko is waving, or motioning, I guess, for the crowd to be still . . . and, there, . . . it . . . is quiet. We listen now as Lisa Peterson translates.

> Comrades. What a joyous occasion for all of the Soviet Union. Modern Soviet science, the envy of the world, has created a miracle. Back after a long journey through the netherworld, our comrade-in-arms, the greatest hero of the Soviet Union, Father of Russia, Vladimir Ilyich Lenin.

Peter, this is Pierre. We are not having audio problems. The crowd is absolutely silent. The man they call Lenin is coming to the microphone. The bands are beginning to play; the crowd is applauding, perhaps a bit politely. He has removed his fur cap, revealing a bald head. And now . . . Lisa Peterson, in Moscow, translating again.

> Comrades. Dear comrades. How good it is to stand with you. To know that the world has changed, but that Soviet Democratic Socialism has not changed. . . . Hear me my people, for there is much for me to tell you. For sixty years the West has told its lies about us. But now I am back, and we shall at last know victory.

> In the coming days, we will speak often. I have much to teach you, and yes, to learn from you as well. The West disputes our miracle today, but soon we shall give them indisputable proof that Lenin is immortal, just as Communism is immortal.

I am tired now. My doctors say I must still gather strength.
My strength is from the people. My rebirth is the people's
victory.

Thank you, Lisa. Peter, if you can hear me, the scene below us
is absolute bedlam. People are singing, crying, laughing, hug-
ging one another. "It is Lenin," they are screaming. I have never
seen anything like this. The Russian people, privately so given
to emotion, publicly so reserved, are showing a new side to
themselves. Everyone is embracing and kissing. This is really
quite moving . . . unbelievable!"

THAT WAS PIERRE SALINGER ON A TAPE NOW
about three hours old. The streets of Moscow once again filled
with traffic and people going about their daily routine. Except
for the reviewing stand, however, Red Square is empty. A light
snow is beginning to fall. The dark clouds overhead appear
ready to put an early end to this very remarkable day. I'm Bob
Zelnick. Back to you, Peter.

FIFTH
DAY

The New York Times

If you hear laughter this morning, it is no doubt from the American right wing. More sensible observers by now realize that, whoever the man they call Lenin may be, the Russians are involved in far more than a practical joke. We, however, watched yesterday's broadcast filled with curiosity about a people whom Western leaders have called the enemy.

Leaving aside the words spoken by Russian politicians, the fact is that a public event took place in the out-of-doors that even Soviet security was unable to contain. In full view of Western cameras, the Russian people acted themselves. This was truly remarkable and, perhaps, more than a bit hopeful.

As for Lenin—or whoever he is—the Soviets have yet to make good on their claim. We doubt they can.

In the meantime, however, we think the Russian people may be more worth watching than Soviet actors. It is good to be reminded that they are not the cold and calculating lot so often described in fiction. Perhaps this drama, the end of which can only be known to Soviet leadership, will have the unintended consequence of understanding at the human level. We hope so.

37

**EXPERT NOTES SOVIET
EXPERIMENTS, CALLS
LENIN STORY POSSIBLE**

Copley News Service

Even as Western leaders strain to get a closer look at the man called Lenin, UCLA physicist Sigmund Horowitz says he recalls the predictions of a Soviet colleague made several years ago.

At that time, Vladimir Rubikov was an intense, frail-looking exchange professor doing work in nuclear medicine at UCLA. Horowitz recalls that the Russian had a reputation for extraordinary brilliance in a field full of the mentally gifted. The two had met at the home of a faculty colleague.

"Rubikov and I had this sort of long conversation about death. It was obvious the Russians were doing a great deal of research in pathology. He also mentioned that suspended animation had been achieved with rats during a Soyuz spaceflight. He even predicted that scientists would soon bring a clinically dead mammal back to life."

Horowitz said that although he discounted the likelihood of success in such experiments, he "did not doubt that some of the best minds in the Soviet Union were working in the field."

"I cannot say anything about this so-called Lenin business, but if it turned out to be true, I would not be altogether astonished," Horowitz said.

The professor is the first U.S. scientist to show any willingness to take this week's major news story seriously. . . .

Daily Worker

LENIN LIVES; WORKERS REJOICE

American comrades have now seen for themselves the miracle of Marxist-Leninist medicine. Millions of Russians and more millions of the world's working people wept for joy upon seeing the People's Hero stand before five hundred thousand comrades and proclaim the "victory of the people."

Scoffing Western news agencies here in the United States were caught completely off-guard by the event. It was obvious to all who knew him that, yes, here was Lenin.

As he stood in Red Square, it was undeniable that the world was witnessing the greatest event since 1917. . . .

EXCLUSIVE
DIXON PREDICTED LENIN STORY
Exclusive to the Enquirer

Psychic Jeane Dixon, a long-time consultant to this publication, revealed today in an exclusive interview that she had predicted the Lenin story in a letter to a friend written in 1959.

"I predicted that before the end of the twentieth century, the Russians would bring back to life a dog and a great man. I said possibly Stalin or Lenin," Dixon stated.

"Now that they've brought back Lenin, I believe they're going to bring back Stalin, too. And the United States will bring back Jack Kennedy. The three will work out world peace."

Confirming the story, Dixon's lifelong friend, Eunice Smith, said she still has the letter but would not sell it at any price. . . .

SIXTH
DAY

WASHINGTON

GOOD EVENING, I'M TOM BROKAW.

Prime Minister Indira Gandhi today became the first world leader to publicly recognize the man called Lenin. Although she did not mention Lenin by name, Mrs. Gandhi did say that she would welcome the visit of all representatives of the Soviet Union, including—and this is a quote—"persons who symbolize great achievements in Soviet science." The Indian leader, however, did not indicate whether any meeting is being planned.

Meanwhile, "chaotic" is the best description of events taking place today in the United Nations. Here with more is NBC diplomatic correspondent Bernard Kalb.

TOM, SPEAKING FOR THE FIRST TIME ON BEHALF of the United States, U.N. Ambassador Jeane Kirkpatrick touched off a furious fight in the General Assembly by charging the Soviet Union with—and I quote now—"a fraud that has gone far enough."

Kirkpatrick was in turn immediately attacked by the delegate from Hungary, who said the United States can be expected to slander the Soviet Union, but that other nations should be willing to wait for evidence. Now to Tom Pettit in Washington.

BERNARD, WORD OF AMBASSADOR KIRKPATRICK'S
charges were relayed swiftly to Washington. Always a city where
people have something to say, this day was no different. Speaking for the Democrats, Senator Alan Cranston of California:

"I AM NATURALLY DISTRESSED AT THE MISMAN-
agement of this issue by the Reagan administration. Up until
now, this was the Russians' story, and they obviously had the
burden of proving it. Besides the fact that we have no evidence to
call it a 'fraud,' we are shifting the burden upon ourselves to
prove a negative. This is a mistake."

AND FOR THE REPUBLICANS, HOWARD BAKER:

"TOM, THE LONGER WE SAY NOTHING ABOUT
this story, the more credibility it unfortunately gains. I just don't
think the president could afford to sit this one out at the risk of a
total propaganda victory for the Soviets."

SEVENTH
DAY

"LENIN" GRANTS INTERVIEW;
MORE CONTACTS SEEN

MOSCOW (UPI)—Alleged former Soviet Premier V. I. Lenin today granted an interview to several journalists, including Pierre Le Clerc of the French daily Le Monde.

Among the many journalists who sought an interview was, reportedly, Barbara Walters of ABC News. Her request was turned down by the Russians with no reason given. ABC News will neither confirm nor deny that the request was made.

According to those who saw him, the man looked remarkably like old photographs of Lenin and showed a detailed knowledge of the Russian Revolution. Although he said he had been reading extensively for the past week, he did profess ignorance of many contemporary events and made several errors of geographic reference.

"Whoever he is, he is a skilled actor," Le Clerc said later, "the best I have ever seen." The journalist also said Lenin proudly displayed an old scar on his neck, suffered during an assassination attempt in 1919. Doctors reportedly removed the bullet in 1922.

"The man was intense, bright, articulate and even likable, I would say. But not modern. This man's view of authority is obviously far more hard-line than that of the current leadership.

He spoke at some length, for example, of the 'scientific concept of dictatorship.'"

Western analysts expressed disappointment that Russian authorities would not permit tape recordings to be made of the session, which lasted thirty-seven minutes in all.

Nevertheless, reporters here were told to expect further "opportunities" to cover the enigmatic figure. . . .

EIGHTH
DAY

A.M.

Los Angeles Times

AN OPPORTUNITY?

The events of the past week have demonstrated that the Soviet Union is prepared to risk a great deal of political credibility on the performance of a single individual. It is, of course, far too early to say whether this man is Lenin.

One thing is clear, however: By shouting "fraud," the Reagan administration is also risking *its* political credibility—a risk, we fear, that is being taken far too lightly. Senator Cranston made a sensible point when he declared the United States was "shifting the burden of proof."

Meanwhile, we think the time has come to consider another aspect of this bizarre case. For reasons known only to themselves, the Soviets have thrust a man upon the world stage who, for now, is of heroic dimensions in Eastern Europe. Leaving aside the grimmer rhetoric of some of his initial comments to a handful of Western journalists, we are intrigued by his potential as a statesman. Lenin was, after all, a great world figure. Even if he has not returned, it is undeniable that the Soviets wish us to think he has.

Rather than the shrill taunts of the Reagan administration—which at best are unseemly and at worst counterproductive—could this be an opportunity to negotiate with a fresh face on the Russian scene? It is a question worth pondering.

51

GALLUP POLL

In a nationwide survey completed Friday, an overwhelming number of adult Americans said they do not believe the Soviet claim to have resurrected the corpse of Vladimir Lenin. Nevertheless, survey results did indicate that a surprising number of those interviewed were "not sure" whom to believe.

The survey, based on 1,031 interviews, represented all portions of the country as well as traditional voting blocs contained in typical Gallup polls. Only one question was asked: "Do you believe that the Russians have resurrected former Premier V. I. Lenin?" Interestingly, almost all (96 percent) of those interviewed expressed some knowledge of the story.

Here are the results:

	Yes	No	Not Sure
Men	9%	72%	19%
Women	7	64	29
North	11	70	19
South	4	79	17
East	13	68	19
West	10	67	23
Aged 20-30	16	65	19
31-45	8	79	13
46-65	9	78	13
Over 65	12	71	17

The sample, which contains a 4 percent margin of error, indicates that the younger (20-30) population does tend to give the story slightly higher credence than their elders. Conceivably, recent motion picture fantasies such as "E.T., The Extra-Terrestrial" have planted the seeds of credibility more widely among those under thirty.

BURBANK, CALIFORNIA

AND NOW . . . HEEEEERE'S JOHNNY!

THANK YOU. THANK YOU. I SEE SOME OF YOU ARE still wearing overcoats. It is cold outside. . . .

How cold is it? Funny you should ask. It is *so* cold that our director flew to Moscow for the winter.

Actually he didn't, but NBC did ask him to assist in the Lenin spectacular. What a story. Can you believe that? I saw a bumper sticker on the Hollywood Freeway this afternoon. It read "If Lenin's back, get out your boots, cuz this is Bul-shevik." . . .

But he looks good for a guy who's been dead sixty years, doesn't he? Doc says he's seen worse.

NINTH
DAY

U.S. News & World Report

Insiders at the White House say U.N. Ambassador Jeane Kirkpatrick won points with her boss for her no-nonsense approach to the Lenin matter. Reagan, aides say, believes the United States should continue to resist firmly the latest propaganda attempt of the Soviet Union. . . .

Meanwhile, State Department officials are fretting that the Lenin story may already be reaping dividends in the Third World, much of which is apparently awestruck by the Soviet claim.

TENTH DAY

OKLAHOMA CITY, OKLAHOMA

FRIENDS, JESUS SAID, "WHATEVER DOST YOU sowest, so shall you also reap." The communists don't know this, of course, because, they don't read the Bible. If they did they wouldn't be communists. It's as simple as that. You see God said, "I am the Lord thy God." God said that Amen, he did. He did not say, "Science shalt you worship." No, he did not. If Jesus raised Lazarus from the dead after only four days, raising Lenin after sixty years would make the Russians better than Jesus. Anyone who thinks that could be so obviously has not read the Bible. Why is something as simple as that so hard for some people to understand?

You know I read in the paper this morning that Mexico has extended an invitation to this Lenin character to visit there? Mexico used to be a Christian nation. I say *used* to be. And Glory be to God, someday she will be again. After, I say *after* the Tribulation. In the meantime, I wouldn't want to live there. . . .

ELEVENTH
DAY

CHINESE WARN PEOPLE
OF SOVIET HOAX

BEIJING (UPI)—After maintaining official silence on the Lenin story for more than a week, the Chinese government now appears anxious to condemn it as a hoax.

Speaking for the Ministry of Information, radio broadcasters today spent more than fifteen minutes of airtime warning the people not to believe the "monstrous lies of hegemonistic powers." Although not mentioning Lenin by name, there was no doubt that he was the subject of official commentaries.

Well-known commentator Ha Ja Kwang, for example, said, "Do not believe the claims of power-mad ghouls, who say their science has created a god. This is an inexcusable deviation from true Marxism."

Western analysts here had wondered how long the Chinese could maintain silence in a country with a common, though closed, border with the Soviets. Today's remarks clearly demonstrate that, by now, most if not all of the population has heard the rumors of Lenin.

Though not officially religious, the Chinese are nonetheless a superstitious people. Claims of a modern resurrection, if verified, could have incalculable implications, analysts here agree.

TWELFTH
DAY

LENIN VISITS
BIRTHPLACE

ULYANOVSK, RUSSIA (UPI) — Former Soviet leader V. I. Lenin—or at least his look-alike—today visited this Volga River town where he was born in 1870. A local holiday having been proclaimed, the national hero was mobbed by school children wherever he went.

In contrast to his strong revolutionary rhetoric of the past several days, believed to have been aimed chiefly at the Third World, today's visit was relegated to mundane matters.

Introduced by the local school superintendent as the valedictorian of his class, parents beamed as he told students to "study hard" for the Russian motherland.

"Someday maybe you will fly in a spaceship," Lenin said with mock seriousness. "I know all about them now. I, too, have been studying hard."

This last remark brought appreciative laughter from the crowd, pleased that Lenin has much catching up to do before he knows as much about the modern world as they.

Outside a fish market, the former premier picked up a small child and kissed her cheek, to the delight of her surprised mother. Not unlike an American politician, everywhere the leader went, he embraced followers and shook hands.

Western journalists, conducting an informal poll among

71

themselves, agreed that whoever he is, he has won solid approval with the masses. This Russian carries himself with the confidence and vigor of a charismatic leader, not seen here since Joseph Stalin. . . .

THIRTEENTH DAY

San Francisco Chronicle

LENIN SPURS COMMERCE
IN BAY AREA
By Theresa Speck

Marxism is okay for bedtime reading, but in the United States of America young communists can't seem to rid themselves of old capitalist habits.

At least that seems to be the case in the Bay Area, where the local chapter of the Revolutionary Workers Party was hawking Lenin T-shirts in Golden Gate Park this past weekend. Five bucks apiece, comrade; ten bucks for sweatshirts.

What will the money go for? Crystal Fleming, organizer of the event, sheepishly admitted that she has "no specific plans."

"Lenin is hot. We just figured it was a good time to cash in on it," she said. . . .

FOURTEENTH DAY

HAMMER MEETS LENIN;
SAYS HE'S CONVINCED

VIENNA (AP) — U.S. industrialist Armand Hammer, a long-time confidant of Soviet leaders, told Western news editors here today that he has had talks with the man called Lenin and is "convinced" of his credentials.

"I suppose this kind of thing is hard for many in the West to swallow, but he is who he says he is, of that I am sure," Dr. Hammer said.

The oil magnate said he had met Lenin in 1922 and is certain this is the same man. "The world has produced few geniuses of Lenin's caliber," Hammer remarked. "While it is not inconceivable to me that someone might look like Lenin, that he might also think like Lenin is impossible. The man I met is the father of Soviet communism."

Hammer was critical of Western leaders who, he said, have a "bigotry" about Russian science. "It is odd because we are ready to believe the Soviets are capable of monstrous inventions in the field of weaponry."

Hammer said he hopes Lenin might play a role in international diplomacy, although he added that he was given no insight as to the former premier's political future in the Soviet Union. "Perhaps an ambassador," he shrugged, adding, "I really don't know."

FIFTEENTH
DAY

HOLLYWOOD, CALIFORNIA

. . . NOW WE JOIN PEGGY JO ABRAHAM AT THE corner of Laurel Canyon and Ventura boulevards, where she has been talking to people as they pass on the sidewalk. Today's question is, "Do you believe Lenin has returned?" Peggy?

THANK YOU, DEBBY. WELL WE HAVE QUITE A crowd of people here, all interested in today's question, so I'll just turn around and let you meet some of them. Hi, there, what's your name?

I'M BOB.

BOB, DO YOU BELIEVE LENIN HAS RETURNED?

YEAH, SORTA . . . I MEAN HE SEEMS REAL, YOU know. . . .

OK, AND HOW ABOUT YOU. WHAT'S YOUR NAME?

I'M DENISE.

DENISE, WHAT DO YOU THINK ABOUT LENIN?

83

FAKE. MOST DEFINITELY. SHUT UP, SUE. THAT'S my friend. She thinks he's cute. Anyway, well, I just believe that, you know, he's been dead like a hundred years or something, so it's impossible.

OK. AND WHAT'S YOUR NAME?

MRS. PACKWOOD.

MRS. PACKWOOD, DO YOU BELIEVE LENIN HAS returned?

WELL, IF YOU ASKED ME A WEEK AGO I'D HAVE told you absolutely not.

AND NOW?

WELL . . . IT IS HARD TO BELIEVE, BUT SOME OF MY friends do, so . . . I say maybe.

DEBBY, YOU HEARD THE VERDICT. ONE YES, ONE no and one maybe, just proving that at least here in the Valley, we are in complete agreement with Messrs. Gallup and Harris.
    In Studio City, I'm Peggy Jo Abraham with Channel 5 Action News.

SIXTEENTH DAY

Los Angeles Times

A TIME FOR REAPPRAISAL

It has now been two weeks since the Soviets shocked the world with the announcement of the return of former premier V. I. Lenin. We admit to scoffing a bit ourselves when this story broke. The credibility of the man called Lenin, however, is no longer the central question, if indeed it ever was.

Appearance and style are easy qualities to imitate. Charisma is another matter. Regardless who the man behind the Lenin mask might be—and we don't discount a grand charade—the fact is that he has won the approval and acceptance of the Russian people. Maturity in international relations requires that we face the world as it exists, not as we would like it to be. For this reason, it is important that the United States deal with him as a force to be reckoned with.

For twenty years, the United States sat out numerous opportunities for rapprochement with China because of our inability to accept the fact that Chiang was in Taiwan and not in Beijing. We hope we have learned something from those tragic years. Whether Lenin is, or ought to be, in his tomb, the fact remains that someone called Lenin is beginning to make life uncomfortable for the West. This is particularly true in our relations with the Third World, which, incidentally, is happily liberated from the semantics of Lenin I versus Lenin II.

In our news space, we have until now dealt gingerly with Western sensitivities on this matter by placing the name Lenin in quotation marks. Beginning with today's edition we have stopped. Lenin lives. It is time for the United States to find out why.

SEVENTEENTH
DAY

The Star

FAYETTEVILLE, N.C. — Two eyewitnesses, giving sworn statements to this publication, say they met V. I. Lenin in 1968. At that time he was traveling under the name of Gork.

Marvin Gossett, 69, and his sister May, 72, each told the story under hypnosis that year, according to reliable medical authorities in this county.

"At that time he had hair, but when we saw Lenin we knew it was him," May said. "You can't forget a face like that," Marvin added.

Gossett, a retired printer, said they first met Gork on a camping trip. "He was looking for his spaceship, but of course he didn't say so. Later we drove him into town. It was then he tried to talk us into taking a trip to his planet. We talked it over but decided no. May, you see, has a bad heart. He told us someday he'd come back and take over the world. . . ."

EIGHTEENTH
DAY

WASHINGTON

THIS IS LARRY KING . . . OMAHA, YOU'RE ON THE line. Give us your first name, please.

LOU.

WHAT'S THE GOOD WORD, LOU? . . . LOU? LOU, turn your radio off.

OH, YEAH . . . JUST A MINUTE.

WHAT'S THE GOOD WORD, LOU?

SAY, LARRY, I LOVE YOUR SHOW . . . LISTEN EVERY night. . . .

THANKS, LOU. WHAT DO YOU WANT TO TALK about?

SAY, UH . . . I JUST WANT TO KNOW YOUR OPINION of Lenin. They say he's coming to the United States.

WELL, LOU, ACTUALLY HE'S COMING TO THE

United Nations. . . .

WELL, THAT'S MY POINT.

WHAT'S YOUR POINT, LOU?

I THINK RONNIE WAS WRONG TO LET HIM COME.

LOU, LENIN WAS INVITED BY THE SECRETARY-general.

WHOEVER. THE MAN'S A COMMUNIST, AND I DON'T think it's right.

LOU, ARE YOU SAYING JUST BECAUSE LENIN IS A communist we should ignore him? Now . . . c'mon, Lou, you don't mean that. Don't you think this is a good chance to find out more about the man and, especially, about *why* he's such a hero in Africa?

I THINK IT'S A GOOD CHANCE FOR SOMEONE TO give him a swift kick in the pants.

WELL, YOU'RE ENTITLED TO YOUR OPINION, OF course, Lou. This is a free country.

A LITTLE TOO FREE IF YOU ASK ME. LARRY, you're an intelligent individual. You must know these people.

WHICH PEOPLE?

THE HEAD HONCHOS, THE BIG SHOTS. . . .

WELL, I KNOW MY ENGINEER HERE, GARY.

LARRY, I'LL BELIEVE IT IF YOU SAY IT'S TRUE, BUT do you think this guy came back from the dead, like they say?

LOU, I'M GOING TO SHOCK YOU. YES, LOU, I believe it.

YOU DO?

YEP.

WELL, I'M GLAD I'M OLD, SO I WON'T HAVE TO SEE what happens next.

THANKS FOR CALLIN', PAL. LITTLE ROCK, YOU'RE on.

NINETEENTH
DAY

LUBBOCK, TEXAS

Calling All Christians! 666 Is Here! Read this booklet. It will only save your soul!

Biblical scholars have pieced together astonishing new evidence that conclusively proves the man they call Lenin is the Antichrist of Bible prophecy.

> But this thou hast: Thou hatest the works of the Nicolaites, which I also hate. (Revelation 2:6)

Who were the Nicolaites whom God hated? "Nicolas" in Greek means "victory of the people." Why should God hate a people's victory? Because of their teachings! (Revelation 2:15) Who was the last czar of Russia, slain in a "victory of the people"? Czar Nicolas. Who gave the orders? Lenin, whose occasional nom de plume was *Nicolai!*

Where did Lenin come from? Simbirsk (presently known as Ulyanovsk) in the Central Asian steppes, near a region called Wormwood. (See your atlas.) "Wormwood" was the name given to the fallen star and the waters made bitter where it landed. (Revelation 8:10, 11)

Lenin fed his people not with grain, but with the "Commu-

101

nist Manifesto," the book that "will make thy stomach bitter, but in thy mouth will be sweet as honey." (Revelation 10:8, 9)

> Here is wisdom. He who has understanding, let him calculate the number of the beast, for it is the number of a man and its number is 666. (Revelation 13:18)

What is Lenin's "number"? Here is a man who was born the third of *six* children, who fluently spoke *six* languages, and who was ruler of Russia *six* years (1918-1924). Now after *sixty* years he has risen from the grave—the beast "that was and that is, giving authority to the first beast, and causing all to worship it." (Revelation 13:11)

ACCEPT JESUS
READ THE BIBLE

THE WHITE HOUSE, WASHINGTON

Your Holiness:

Greetings from the United States.

As you know, the two of us have shared a dreadful experience that has brought us to a closer communion with God. I think we both know that all of the powers of science cannot match the power of a single prayer. In the past week, "our friends" in the East would have the world forget its faith in the Almighty altogether with a callous and calculated lie on a scale the world has never before seen. I, of course, refer to the Lenin matter.

I have tried to remain calm and detached from all of this, but it has not been easy. Now, I fear if something is not done, so much of what we have both worked for, in our separate ways of course, will be lost.

The purpose of this letter is to express my hope that you might be able to say the words that I cannot find. That together we might restore Truth—and God—on earth.

Faithfully,

TWENTIETH DAY

EVANS and NOVAK

NEW YORK — A growing debate is occurring in the Reagan administration concerning the appropriate posture to be taken during the Lenin visit here in ten days. Associates close to national security adviser Robert McFarlane say he is adamant that the United States not lend dignity to what the president considers a sham. The action presumably favored by administration hard-liners is for the U.S. mission to be conspicuously absent for the grand event.

Meanwhile at Foggy Bottom, State Department careerists are said to have gained some sympathy from Secretary of State George Shultz for a more moderate approach, namely the absence of Ambassador Kirkpatrick. Although no one has yet suggested that Shultz and McFarlane are on a collision course over this matter, Shultz will soon be required to make his final recommendation to the president.

Lenin has not yet become a strong partisan issue in this country mainly because the politicians of each party are fearful of going out on a limb one way or the other. Even liberals, who generally favor a softer approach toward Moscow, are still a bit leery of getting burned on the identification issue. In recent days, therefore, a movement has been building to defuse it with an end run. By declaring it to be immaterial to our continuing bilateral relations, the American Left is beginning to make the case that, call him anything you like, this Lenin is a genuine spokesman for Moscow. On that basis, they argue, he should be accorded appropriate recognition as a visiting statesman.

A walkout by the U.S. mission, therefore, would amount to a throwing down of the gauntlet both domestically and internationally. Our sources say that moderate Republicans in Congress are more than a bit apprehensive that the McFarlane-Meese faction will bite off more than the president can reasonably chew and complicate further his tenuous relationship with the legislative branch.

The other noteworthy aspect of this case is that, despite the latter-day Lenin's instant popularity with his own countrymen and the warm welcome given him last week in India, his only role at this point seems to be that of communist elder statesman. So far as anyone knows, the Politburo is still in firm control of the party and the country. There is no indication that this is about to change. Thus the argument runs, why treat Mr. Lenin as a villain before he does anything villainous?

Colonel McFarlane's answer to the president—why give him the opportunity?

TWENTY-FIRST
DAY

LOS ANGELES

THIS IS KABC TALK RADIO. I'M KEN MINYARD along with Bob Arthur. . . . And now it's time for Bruce Hershensohn. Good morning, Bruce!

HI, KEN; HI, BOB.

LET'S SEE, BRUCE, TODAY YOU'RE GOING TO TALK about . . . Bruce, you're breaking your promise. . . .

KEN, I KNOW TWO WEEKS AGO I SAID I WASN'T going to say anything more about Lenin, and you're right, I *am* breaking my promise. Really, I knew I shouldn't be making it at the time. . . .

WELL, JUST TO SHOW YOU WHAT NICE GUYS WE are, we won't say we knew it all along.

OH, GO AHEAD AND SAY IT.

OK, BRUCE.

KEN, THE THING THAT MOST UPSETS ME ABOUT this whole business of Lenin visiting the United Nations is that we've got all the arguments—both for and against—backward, we really have. Before I get ahead of myself, though, let me give you just a little background to help put this matter in some perspective.

Back in 1918, when Lenin (or if you prefer, Lenin the First) was consolidating his power shortly after the fall of czarist Russia, a communist from a rival faction tried to assassinate him. Though he was badly wounded, the point is that he lived. And do you know what his fellow Bolsheviks did? They immediately rounded up five hundred men and women suspected—just suspected, mind you—of being aligned with the opposing faction and killed them. No kangaroo court or any other nicety, just *bang*. Was Lenin aware of this? Of course he was aware of it, they were his own friends who did it.

Well regardless of what you thought of the czar, this started a killing spree that lasted through the time of Stalin and, really—if you want to be honest about it—through to Andropov as well. In all, millions upon millions of Russians—some estimates go as high as ninety million—were eventually killed, not because they were czarists, but because they made the mistake of being educated or affluent or, most often, on the losing side of a political power play.

This has been the sickening history of communism, Russian style. And who is the "father of communism"? According to the Russians, it isn't Marx and it isn't Engels, it is Lenin.

Lenin's theory of government was nothing more than ruthless dictatorship. This isn't my assessment, it's his own. Let me quote you something he wrote as premier in 1920.

> The scientific concept of dictatorship means neither more nor less than unlimited power resting directly on force, not limited by anything, nor restrained by any laws or absolute rules. Nothing else but that.

112

Now if that isn't chilling, I don't know what is, except that there is more, much more. Let me give you just one other example. Quote:

> The communists must be prepared to make every sacrifice and, if necessary, even resort to all sorts of cunning, schemes, and strategems to employ illegal methods, to evade and conceal the truth. . . . The practical part of communist policy is to incite one against another. . . . We communists must use one country against another. . . .

There is a lot more, Ken, but time does not permit.

Just let me conclude where I started. If I could sum up the reasons given so far *against* Lenin's visit—by the president's people—it is that he is *not* who he says he is; he is *not* the real Lenin. The side in *favor* of his visit, and by this I'm really referring to the Third World leaders who got him invited in the first place, is that he *is* who he says he is: the *original Lenin.*

The trouble with this is obvious. If the man is a charlatan, a fraud, at least we can hope that he won't stand for the very worst things the communists have ever said about themselves. Perhaps he'll even be willing to give communism a new tone or emphasis, though I doubt it.

If he *is* Lenin, look out! This man doesn't belong within ten thousand miles of the United Nations. The president, however, opposes him because he says the man is a fraud, and I just think that is most unfortunate. Ken?

OK, BRUCE, BUT HE *IS* COMING, SO WHAT DO WE DO now?

WE WALK OUT.

113

BECAUSE YOU THINK HE IS LENIN? I MEAN . . . WELL what are you saying?

KEN, I DO NOT THINK PERSONALLY THAT HE IS Lenin, but we ought to really let the world understand that this is far more than a question of identification.

BRUCE, "EVERYTHING'S GOING TO BE OK"— egbok, fella. . . .

WELL KEN, I SAY THAT TO MYSELF ABOUT TWICE A day now, but somehow I just don't know.

OK, WELL THANK YOU, BRUCE. . . .

KEN, CAN I SAY JUST ONE MORE THING? . . .

VERY QUICKLY.

KEN, VERY QUICKLY, DO YOU REMEMBER LENIN'S first speech, less than three weeks ago?

SURE.

AT THAT TIME HE SAID THE RUSSIANS WOULD soon provide indisputable medical proof? Well *then*, virtually everyone here pooh-poohed it. *Now*, having given us absolutely no proof at all—but a whole lot of political rhetoric—what is it, nearly half the country thinks this guy's for real, according to last night's NBC poll?

THE BIG LIE TECHNIQUE—IS THAT WHAT YOU'RE saying?

THE BIG LIE IS RIGHT, BOB.

OK, WELL THANK YOU VERY MUCH, BRUCE, AND
we'll talk to you again tomorrow.

DEAR ABBY: We have always been God-fearing people. I
have tried to raise my sons with respect and decency. Now Ed
(not his real name) has taken up with a girl who told him she
worships Lenin. If I told my husband, he would have a heart
attack. Should I try to break up their relationship? Ed is only 17.
WORRIED IN DENVER

DEAR WORRIED: This phenomenon is obviously very
recent and will probably pass soon. Youthful fads can come and
go very quickly. I would advise Ed not to mention this to your
husband. You have not said how Ed feels about her religious
practice. He may think it is as far-out as you do.

TWENTY-SECOND
DAY

VATICAN CITY (AP) — Speaking on Vatican radio today, Pope John Paul II issued the Church's strongest challenge yet to what he called "the growing cult of Lenin."

Decrying the worldwide phenomenon as "apostasy"—infidelity to Church teachings—the pontiff, for the first time, took direct aim at the Lenin affair. Previously, the Roman Catholic Church had seemed to regard the increasing popularity of the former Russian leader as a political matter.

It is clear from today's broadcast, however, that the pontiff, himself a charismatic world figure, regards Lenin as a direct threat to Christianity.

Speaking metaphorically, the pope referred to the "tail of the dragon" sweeping the entire world. The reference was obviously intended to underscore the pope's belief that communism is the diabolically inspired archenemy of Christianity.

Calling on fellow Poles, in particular, to increase their devotion to the Madonna of Czestochowa, the pope seemed particularly concerned with reports of a growing fascination with Lenin by Eastern Europeans.

The Catholic leader surprised even veteran observers of the Vatican, however, with the suggestion that the Lenin appear-

119

ance at the United Nations next week "may mark the final confrontation between the Gospel and the anti-Gospel."

"Human resurrection is blasphemy," the pope declared. "Christus vincit, Christus imperat, Christus regnat." (Christ conquers, Christ commands, Christ rules.)

TWENTY-THIRD
DAY

SOLZHENITSYN SCOLDS WEST;
LENIN "GREATEST LIE"

ANN ARBOR (UPI) — In a speech before students and faculty at the University of Michigan, Aleksandr Solzhenitsyn today repeated his charges that the resurrection of Lenin is the Soviet Union's "greatest lie."

"That the West watches hypnotically while the snake charmer performs his magic is a disgrace," the exiled author said.

"The president of the United States alone has the courage to call this an evil falsehood, but other Western leaders cower shamelessly behind the cloak of 'diplomacy.' Today that word means 'cowardice,'" he said.

Solzhenitsyn said he believes the Russian claim could never have been made successfully at any other time in history. "The West has slipped irretrievably into the abyss of decadence. It will now accept any lie, allow any monster to sit on its doorstep, in the name of security."

The one-time dissident, who wrote of his life in the Russian Gulag, said it is "irresponsible" to point blame at Eastern European and Third World nations that have taken to Lenin. "Only the West could have stopped the avalanche. I fear we are now doomed. . . ."

TWENTY-FOURTH
DAY

WASHINGTON

GOOD EVENING, I'M TED KOPPEL AND THIS IS "Nightline." Tonight we look at the growing events involving perhaps the most bizarre news story of this century: The Russian claim of having resurrected former Soviet Premier Vladimir Ilyich Lenin.

Mr. Lenin—or at least someone playing the part with virtuosity until now—is due to arrive here in New York next Wednesday night amidst what we are told will be the greatest security arrangements ever made for a world figure.

We have two guests with us this evening: In Washington, Director William Casey of the Central Intelligence Agency and in Moscow, Vladimir Posner, who has appeared before on this program. Mr. Posner is a correspondent for Radio Moscow.

We'll begin with Mr. Posner.

Vladimir, may I say, as always, how very good it is for you to take the time to be on this program.

TED, BEING WITH YOU IS ALWAYS A PLEASURE.

I SUPPOSE I SHOULD START BY TELLING YOU that nearly half of our audience tonight simply disbelieves that this is the real Lenin. How do you respond to that?

127

MR. KOPPEL, I UNDERSTAND HOW DIFFICULT IT IS for people in nations not yet having had the opportunity to meet Premier Lenin to grasp the significance of this achievement. I would simply ask your audience to keep an open mind and to evaluate Mr. Lenin, not by what they may have read in Western journals, but by listening to him and seeing him while he is in your country.

FORGIVE ME, VLADIMIR, BUT ISN'T THAT JUST A little unfair? After all, your country had offered to make scientific evidence available shortly after the announcement of the resurrection. Watching a human performance at the United Nations can hardly be the kind of proof those who sincerely doubt this story can find reassuring.

TED, AS YOU KNOW, I AM NOT A MEMBER OF THE government, and, therefore, I cannot tell you precisely what scientific evidence can be made available considering the national security ramifications. . . .

OK, WELL LET'S JUST HOLD IT ON THAT POINT for a moment. Are you saying that Soviet security is jeopardized by revealing how you raised a corpse from the dead?

IT IS POSSIBLE, YES, TED, BUT AGAIN THAT IS NOT for me to say.

WELL, NOW, SURELY YOU DON'T INTEND TO TANtalize us. Are we going to be offered proof?

TED, IN TIME, YES I'M SURE ARRANGEMENTS FOR A scientific exchange may be made. I just think that for now, these things may be a little premature.

128

ALL RIGHT. LET'S GO TO MR. CASEY. MR. DIRECtor, you have heard Mr. Posner. Is your agency aware of anything at all that would give credence to, or cast doubt upon, the Soviet claim?

I DON'T PRETEND WE KNOW EVERYTHING THAT goes on inside Russia. If we did, we would not need to ask for verification in arms negotiations, but in answer to your question, the answer is no. I might say that the intelligence-gathering agencies of our friends throughout the world agree with this conclusion. . . .

EXCUSE ME, MR. CASEY, BUT WHAT CONCLUSION?

WE DO NOT BELIEVE THAT THE RUSSIANS HAVE performed a medical resurrection. In fact, let me go further by telling you that—for reasons I may not go into—that Lenin was actually cremated over thirty-five years ago.

MR. POSNER, THAT IS A FAIRLY SERIOUS CHARGE. How do you respond?

WELL, TED, I AM A BIT DISAPPOINTED THAT YOU have not pressed Mr. Casey in the same manner you pressed me a moment ago. He has just made an outrageous statement, for which he will give no proof whatsoever.

FAIR ENOUGH, MR. CASEY, MR. POSNER HAS SOMEthing there. Is this a Mexican standoff? Is each side going to ask the American people to take these claims on faith?

TED, I DON'T FEEL WE HAVE THE BURDEN OF

proof. After all, we haven't resurrected Abraham Lincoln. If we did, I think we'd owe it to the world to show how we did it.

OK, WELL GENTLEMEN, IF I MAY, LET'S SHIFT SUB-jects here in the interest of time. Mr. Posner, if you would, give us your best guess as to what Mr. Lenin will tell the world next week here in New York.

TED, OBVIOUSLY I AM IN NO POSITION TO SPEAK for the premier, except to tell you it is an open record what he has talked about already. He is manifestly a man of peace, a man of the people, with sincere ambition for the working classes to better themselves economically. . . .

EXCUSE ME, VLADIMIR, YOU HAVE REFERRED TO Mr. Lenin as "the premier" now several times. Do I detect more than simple deference to his former rank?

SIMPLE DEFERENCE, AS YOU PUT IT, THAT IS ALL.

ALL RIGHT, MR. CASEY, THE PRESIDENT HAS MADE it clear he is against this visit and has called it a "sham" on his weekly radio broadcast. You heard Mr. Posner. If Mr. Lenin is a man of peace, doesn't it seem fair to let him speak before reacting so, well, some would say "stridently" to this event?

IT DOESN'T MATTER WHAT LENIN MAY ACTUALLY say or not say at the United Nations. He is being built up daily as a hero of unimaginable proportions by revolutionaries around the world. Yasir Arafat has proclaimed the PLO will fight in the name of Lenin; his statue recently has been erected in Managua at a huge public celebration. The U.N. visit will add unbelievably to the momentum of international revolutionary and terrorist activities.

OK, HOW ABOUT IT, MR. POSNER? MUCH THAT troubles the West is happening right now in the name of Vladimir Lenin.

WELL, TED, I AM SORRY THE WEST IS TROUBLED, but you see we have very little control over how someone feels about Premier Lenin. It is true that there has been an outpouring of love for him in many parts of the world. The few of our countrymen who remember seeing and hearing Lenin when they were very young say this is to be expected. He is a very captivating, charismatic leader. Let me just add that I personally think it quite unfair of your president to politicize what has otherwise been an apolitical event. It just contributes to international tensions and otherwise proves nothing.

TELL US ABOUT HIS FUTURE IF YOU WOULD?

TED, I DON'T THINK THAT HAS BEEN DETERMINED —by Premier Lenin or anyone else. It is for now enough that he is back with us.

MR. CASEY, A FINAL WORD?

TED, I HOPE NONE OF YOUR LISTENERS ARE taken in by anything. The American people expect and deserve proof.

MR. POSNER, A BRIEF RESPONSE?

AS I SAID EARLIER, KEEP AN OPEN MIND.

WELL, GENTLEMEN, THAT INDEED IS ALL WE HAVE time for. Thank you both very much for taking the time to be with us.

I'll be back with the last word when we return.

TWENTY-FIFTH DAY

Time Magazine

RELIGION—
NEW ANSWERS TO OLD RIDDLES?

Writing to his fellow ecclesiastics in the second century, St. Irenaeus ominously suggested that attempting to decipher St. John the Apostle's apocalyptic reference to the number 666 (the Antichrist) was ill-advised.

Though modern evangelists can scarcely resist the temptation of playing this "numbers game," with rare exceptions, Roman Catholic commentators have been reluctant to follow suit, the last great Catholic sermons on the subject having been written over one hundred years ago by John Henry Cardinal Newman, the ex-Anglican.

Among Catholic religious themselves, however, 1980 may have been a watershed year with the attempted assassination of the pope—a trigger many say was pulled in Moscow. While outwardly reticent, it is clear that many church officials saw the event as being of portentously apocalyptic significance—an overt assault on the citadel of Christendom. The church's previous enthusiasm for liturgical renewal, begun at Vatican II, has thus waned in light of more basic priorities.

Enter Rev. Ricardo de Vicente, S.J., who has now provoked a storm of controversy that may yet be a precursor to a revolt against the magisterium of Rome. With apparent Vatican approval, de Vicente has cautiously set forth a theory to explain

John's ancient eschatological riddle (Revelation 13:18). His version of 666, though complicated, can be summed up briefly as follows:

Beginning with the fact that Revelation was written in Greek, de Vicente explains, consider that until shortly before the first century the Greeks used letters as substitutes for the numbers one through nine. At that time, the Phoenician letter *bau* ($\digamma$) was used as the number six, *zeta* (ζ) otherwise being the sixth letter of the Greek alphabet. Since the lowercase *zeta* and *bau* are somewhat similar in their sicklelike appearance, de Vicente argues that the religious world might be looking for numbers where it should be looking for symbols—particularly *baus* and *zetas*.

Warming to his theory, de Vicente notes that the Greek letter *rho* (P) is often used in the church as one half of the symbol ☧ or *chi rho*, which is a pictogram of a man (P) on a cross (X), signifying Christ. The "number of a man" being 666 may be no more than *bau bau bau rho*, he says, which visually at least, is close to the Soviet acronym CCCP, meaning USSR. De Vicente's theory goes further, showing other intriguing possibilities by transliterating Greek letters to Russian, but in the end each of his conclusions consistently returns to CCCP as the "number" of the Antichrist. The Chicago-born cleric adds spice to his recipe by noting that just as *chi rho* (☧) can mean Christ, *bau rho*, reversed as in the mirror, resembles a familiar symbol: ⚒.

De Vicente says what originally led him to look for letters instead of numbers was John's thrice-used metaphor, "I am the *alpha* and the *omega*." "I believed this might be an important clue to the author's mind, describing infinity with letters rather than quantum. So I looked for a cryptographic answer to 666."

That he did not follow the admonition of Irenaeus is the least of de Vicente's problems. He has stirred up a hornet's nest among fellow Catholic religious, some of whom had been heralding "liberation theology," that is, that Marxism is the secular side of Christianity. In Latin America, such a controversy is far more than a debate among theoreticians seeking new answers to old riddles. (*See* World.)

TWENTY-SIXTH DAY

LENIN PEACE PROPOSAL SEEN

NEW YORK (UPI) — Sources close to a high-ranking East-European diplomat said here today that Lenin will offer a peace proposal of "breathtaking" originality and scope.

The news sparked a sharp rally on the New York Stock Exchange, which closed up 12 points above yesterday's year-low of 986.

State Department officials, however, reacted by saying that it would be "foolish" to place hope in undisclosed rumors, noting that thus far the Soviet figure has said little that hasn't already been proposed by the Kremlin over the past twelve months.

At the Boston headquarters of Peace Now, however, anti-war activist Julia Stockman said she "fully expects" a major break-through in arms negotiations to be initiated by Lenin. "Above all others, he is the man-of-the-century," Stockman said. . . .

TWENTY-SEVENTH DAY

SCORES ARRESTED AT PEACE DEMONSTRATION; INJURIES REPORTED

WASHINGTON (AP) — This nation's largest peace demonstration since the Vietnam War ended in violence here today, as dozens were injured, several seriously, in noisy, often bitter confrontations with capital police.

By nightfall, the city was calm as local officials here began processing nearly 250 arrests made during the course of a rancorous afternoon.

Earlier in the day, observers noted that things had gone remarkably well as more than 350,000 demonstrators had appeared to be in an almost festive mood, listening to anti-war speakers and celebrated rock groups on the steps of the Lincoln Memorial.

Even as the bright skies overhead turned cloudy, however, capital police braced for a change of climate below when one speaker after another urged the huge audience to "cross the (Arlington) bridge" in the direction of the Pentagon. The call was obviously a challenge to President Reagan, who vowed earlier this week to halt any attempt to disrupt work at the headquarters of the nation's military.

Fighting, however, apparently did not break out until a small band of neo-Nazis appeared on the fringe of the scene with signs reading "Death to Lenin," obviously provoking many pro-

145

Leninists, who had been marching behind banners paying tribute to the former Soviet leader.

The Nazis were quickly dispersed by police but too late to prevent the ensuing rain of rocks and bottles, often thrown indiscriminately.

Thus began an ugly scene reminiscent of the 1960s, with police in full riot gear clubbing demonstrators and in the process occasionally getting roughed up themselves as well. One policeman was later admitted to Georgetown University Medical Center. Doctors there say he will be held overnight for observation of a possible concussion.

Meanwhile, much of the crowd seemed oblivious to the fighting only a short distance away, as it prepared to cross the bridge in a confrontation with the military.

As it turned out, however, the bridge was impassable, having been closed earlier to clean thousands of gallons of spilled oil from an accident last night involving an overturned tanker. Fire department officials proceeded to arrest several persistent marchers, who were attempting to wade, slide and stumble through the foam-covered goo. Early morning Washington traffic had been badly snarled as motorists sought alternate routes into the city.

Demonstration leaders, unaware of the previous night's accident, later angrily charged President Reagan with having deliberately blocked the bridge, vowing next time they would "throw a match." The president and first lady meanwhile were said to be at Camp David and only "heard about" the incident on the radio.

TWENTY-EIGHTH DAY

U.S. TO WALK OUT

WASHINGTON (AP) — Following weeks of controversy within the administration itself, President Reagan has given the order for U.N. Ambassador Jeane Kirkpatrick to lead an exit by her delegation before the arrival of former Soviet Premier V. I. Lenin Wednesday.

At a hastily called press conference, the president read a brief statement in which he said the "United States will not lend dignity to the charade of a speech by a dead man. Somebody had better say that, dressed as he is, the emperor is going to catch a chill."

The announcement touched off angry reactions on Capitol Hill, where Democrats charged the administration with "needlessly provoking" a confrontation with the Soviets.

"The president's behavior is insulting and childish," said Sen. Edward Kennedy (D-Mass.). "I cannot believe that any good can come from showing that we can be as ill-mannered and boorish as (the late Soviet premier) Khrushchev."

House Speaker Thomas P. O'Neill (D-Mass.) said, "He has been listening to all the wrong people. The ultra-right wing in this country has caught the president up in its hysteria. . . . The fact is, this man (Lenin) is an official representative of the other superpower. For God's sake, when are we going to grow up?"

An even angrier response came from Sen. Alan Cranston (D-Calif.), who charged, "He (Reagan) has set peace back about one hundred years. He has simply lost his mind."

TWENTY-NINTH DAY

MOSCOW

Comrades:

When each of you is handed this letter, I will be over the North Atlantic. As we have said, tomorrow will be a great victoi y.

When you hear my address, do not be alarmed that I am deviating from our script. Trust that all along, I have known how we must now proceed.

You have called me a great genius of the theater, and perhaps that is true. But have you also not wondered who I really am? I think so.

Ilya, when your career was eclipsed, seemingly forever, in your heart did you not call out to me for help?

And you, Boris, that misspent summer with Raya not only almost cost you your career but your marriage as well. Did you not secretly guess that it was I who intervened?

The course of communism, indeed the world, is in my hands now. You may retain your fanciful titles, so long as you remember who is Lenin.

If Lazarev should try to give you foolish plans concerning my health, exile him.

You are saying, "But we made this Lenin; we can rid ourselves of him, too."—is it not so? No, dear friends, it is I who have made

153

you. You cannot destroy me, for the people would not permit it. Besides, your own plans are too far along to go back.

I have returned. The "specter of communism" is at last revealed.

Lenin

MAY DAY, MAY DAY. THIS IS AEROFLOT 171. WE
HAVE BEEN . . .

THIRTIETH
DAY

NEW YORK

THIS IS A CBS SPECIAL REPORT. THE COAST GUARD says there are no known survivors of this morning's tragic Russian airline crash in New York Harbor.

Navy divers are still pulling bodies from the scene. The huge Soviet delegation—sixty-seven in all—is the largest contingent of government officials ever to die aboard an airliner in aviation history.

President Reagan has expressed his profound sympathy on behalf of the American people to the Soviet Union and the families of the deceased.

U.N. Secretary-General Javier Perez de Cuellar has adjourned today's session of the General Assembly in mourning for the dead.

Repeating our earlier announcement, we must assume at this moment that former Soviet Premier Vladimir Lenin is among the victims, although we have not received official confirmation from Moscow.

We only know through informed sources that at this moment the Supreme Soviet is meeting in the Kremlin. We go now to CBS correspondent Charles Kuralt, who is standing by at the scene of the crash. . . .

THIRTY-FIRST
DAY

The Washington Post

THE LAND OF THE LOST

In yesterday's twilight we saw the stooped figure of a man carrying a briefcase walk past our window, his overcoat flapping in the wind. He was, no doubt, one of this city's nameless bureaucrats, heading for the Metro station, his day's job done. Governments the world over are populated by servants such as these, who faithfully spend their careers in the service of policymakers.

If the step of last night's pedestrian was a little slower than usual and his stoop a little more pronounced, it was perhaps caused by the knowledge that his government had lost the greatest opportunity within his lifetime to change the world for the better. In the end, however, it was presumably fog and pilot error, not the mindless stubbornness of his leaders, that ended this chance for peace.

Civilizations are carried forward by the small daily steps of our passersby. Occasionally, however, a giant stride occurs when one or two people of great vision are given time enough to lead and their careers are not truncated by disease, war . . . or airline crashes.

The Russians will miss this Lenin—perhaps more than the one before him. We see no other of their people capable of bridging East and West with the charisma and hope he brought to this age, too long now at the precipice.

Until someday another comes to take his place, we must count upon the slow, sure-footed pace of pedestrians to move the world onward.

A haunting question will doubtless be asked by those too ignorant to know it is the wrong question. Did Lenin live? He lived in the hearts of those who believed in him. Somewhere on the grimy, polluted bottom of New York Harbor he is now at final rest. Does Lenin's spirit live? The answer to *that* question remains to be seen.

Meanwhile, it is late, and we too must hurry to the Metro.